By Request

DANDY and BEANO

The Golden Years Volume II

Printed and Published in Great Britain by D. C. Thomson & Co., Ltd.,
185 Fleet Street, London, EC4A 2HS.

© D. C. THOMSON & CO. LTD. 1989.
ISBN 0-85116-436-6

The endpapers featuring Jonah originally appeared in the 1961 Beano Book.

(Certain stories do not appear exactly as originally published.)

It doesn't matter whether DANDY and BEANO stories are set in Sheffield or Shanghai, Britain's best-loved comics always see the funny side. Even during their many forays into the old American West, where a trigger-happy hoodlum would fill you full of lead because he didn't like the colour of your socks, DANDY and BEANO ensured that in their pages, the Wild West became the . . .

...WAY-OUT WEST

COWBOYS AND INDIANS

Remember those legendary cowboys, Wyatt Earp, Billy The Kid, Jesse James, **Whoopee Hank . . .** What? Never heard of **Whoopee Hank?** Okay! Maybe he didn't become a Wild West legend, but he did appear in the earliest issues of BEANO, hanging out with hombres like Lord Snooty and his pals, and that must make him kinda famous.

But one guy who is most definitely a legend is **Little Plum —** a BEANO star of more than three decades — a pint-sized Red Indian brave who could turn any paleface into a smiling face. Here's the proof, from 7th October, 1961.

Waging war on The Puttyfeet Tribe wasn't the only excitement in **Plum's** life. In the wilds, danger lurked behind every rock and tree, in the shape of the grizzliest bunch of bears to be found on either side of The Rockies.

Red Indians and Grizzlies may not see eye to eye (Little Plum would have to be Big Plum to do that) but the bothersome bruins were voted a big hit by BEANO readers. So much so, that in 1960 three of their number were given a regular page of their own. The story below appeared on 28th January, 1961.

By Request

This gun-slingin' gal's name sure rings a bell. That's because it's **Ding Dong Belle.** A Wild West star in BEANOS of yesteryear, Belle was as tough as the guys and bigger than most of 'em!

Well that's enough about The Wild West. Now for something completely diff . . .

HOLD IT RIGHT THERE!
WHAT ABOUT LIL' OL' ME?

Er, and of course one cowboy we could never forget (well, almost never) is **Desperate Dan,** DANDY stalwart for over half a century and the only comic star big enough to make Ding Dong Belle look petite.

Dan's changed very little over the years. Compare the current, cow-pie chompin' figure on the left with the back scratchin', bear-bustin' guy of 50 years earlier.

But **Dan** doesn't spend all his time out where the buffalo roam as you'll see from the page opposite. The Texas tough guy's at a garden party of all things.

QUICK, JOE, SCRAT... ...AN, MY BACK— IT'S ...RE SO ITCHY! ...GH I GUESS ...D BETTER USE THIS RAKE!

HARDER, JOE, HARDER!

AW, HAVE A HEART, DAN. THIS IS MAKING ME DEAD TIRED!

PUFF

WELL, THAT AIN'T GOT RID OF THE ITCH, BUT THIS STAGE COACH MIGHT HELP!

JUMPING CATS! DAN'S BUST MY RAKE!!

I'LL LASSO THE COACH AND LET IT DRAG ME ALONG THE ROAD!

GRIND

HELP!

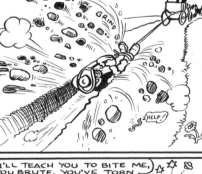

GOSH! MY BACK'S STILL ITCHY!— BUT GEE! THIS BEAR'S GOT MIGHTY SHARP CLAWS— MAYBE THEY'LL DO THE TRICK!

HA! HA! THE BRUTE'LL CLAW MY BACK AND GET RID OF THE ITCH FOR ME— HEY!!

I'LL TEACH YOU TO BITE ME, YOU BRUTE. YOU'VE TORN MY BEST TROUSERS— TAKE THAT!!

WHAM

BROKEN TEETH

GEE! THIS IS GREAT! GUESS I'LL TAKE THE WHOLE FENCE HOME AND KEEP IT THERE AS A BACK-SCRATCHER!

HAVING A WHALE OF A TIME

Back in 1949, no-one had heard the phrase 'Save The Whale' or realised these magnificent creatures would soon be in danger of extinction. The one thing DANDY readers did know about whales was that they were the ideal size for a **Desperate Dan** story.

By Request

But even comic superstars, who are legends in their own lunchtime, need an education. Here's a scene from **Dan's** schooldays

FRONT ROW (left to right) — Miss CONKY HONKER (Infant Teacher), GORDON ZOLA, SAILOR MANN, DESPERATE DAN, GOONY GUBBINS, GOOSEY BERRY, MATILDA MUTCH, BUBBLY BILLY BOGGS, TEENY TWISTLE, Miss MADELEINE HATTER (Primary Teacher).

SECOND ROW (left to right) — Miss FRUITY TOOT (Form 1 Teacher), TITCH FITCH, NIGEL NUTT, SPECKY PEARSON, The Head — FUNGUS-FACE BEARDMORE, Mrs BEARDMORE, CLAUDE HOPPER, DOZY DAY, PODGY RODGERS, Mr FRANK ENSTEIN (Form II Teacher).

SCHOOL

NO WUR KIS DUN ERE

THIRD ROW (left to right) — Mr DROOPY TASH (Form III Teacher), POLLY DOODLE, PENNY FARTHINGALE, BERTHA BELCH, GERALDINE GUFFY, CYNTHIA THMITH, MARGIE REEN, BANDY LEGGAT, GRABBER SNATCH, Mr PUDDING-FACE SQUELCH (Form IV Teacher).

BACK ROW (left to right) — SMUGGY SMART, GUSSY GOOF, HAPPY HARRY HUMPH, PIGGY HOGG, JACK DAW, LANKY LONGBOTTOM (Legs Only).

SHORT STORIES . . . LONG LAU

GOOD KING COKE from Beano

KEYHOLE KATE from Dandy

THE MAGIC LOLLIPOPS from Beano

During DANDY and BEANO'S early years, many of the most amusing moments were provided by strips — three to a page — short on pictures but long on laughs.

BARNEY BOKO from Dandy

MEDDLESOME MATTY from Dandy

DENNIS'S BIG DAY OUT!

What better way to celebrate your comic's 50th birthday than with a trip to London. That was what Dennis did on Friday, 29th July, 1988, the eve of BEANO'S half century.

Being a youngster (a mere 37 at the time) the world's greatest menace couldn't go to the big city on his own, so Euan Kerr, BEANO'S editor, joined him and was even "persuaded" to carry Dennis piggy-back at one point. (What a softy!)

After visiting Tower Bridge, Dennis headed on to the posh Savoy Hotel where journalist William Marshall donned a Lord Snooty outfit for the occasion.

And the thrilling day didn't end there. Dennis and Euan spent the evening chatting to a bloke called Terry Wogan, a conversation that was overheard by several million TV viewers.

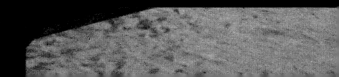

The two comics' cover stars, Korky and Biffo, traditionally appeared in an eggstra-special story for Easter, and even Dandy tough guy Desperate Dan kept the Easter theme rolling along in this early adventure from 8th April, 1939.

NO YOLKING MATTER

When it comes to wise-cracking comic characters, DANDY and BEANO have had their share, but if you happen to be Humpty Dumpty, cracks are no laughing matter, as **Pansy Potter** discovered in this Easter number from 1952.

TOM THUMB

The BEANO'S little big man! **Tom Thumb** was no Daley Thompson but he was certainly the best all-rounder in his class. The scenes below, and the story beginning overleaf, show **Tom** as the little man with the big heart . . .

1 — Through the icy-green waters of the North Sea, not far from the coast of Norway, tore a baby whale. Sunk in its flesh was a Viking harpoon, and clinging to the harpoon's shaft were Tom Thumb and his little friend Tinkel. The midget pair had come through many adventures since they left England, but never had they been in greater peril than now. Attached to the harpoon was a stout rope which led back to a Viking rowboat, where several Norse whale-hunters clung on grimly.

2 — "H-hold tight!" gasped Tom, spitting out salt water as he spoke. The words had hardly left Tom's frozen lips when the baby whale, driven frantic by the harpoon in its back, made a great effort to free itself. Tom and Tink were engulfed in a deluge of icy sea-water as the big fish dived slightly, then — Whoosh! The young whale heaved itself high out of the water. The sudden wrench tore the harpoon from the whale's back and the barbed weapon dropped into the sea.

3 — Aboard the Viking rowboat, loud cries of disappointment went up as the harpoon-rope suddenly slackened. The Norsemen crowded to the gunwale to watch the baby whale blowing water high in the air as it made off. When Olaf, the six-foot fair-haired leader of the hunters hauled the harpoon clear of the water, however, the big Viking grunted in surprise. For, still clinging to the harpoon's shaft, he saw Tom and Tinkel!

4 — In a moment, the harpoon was aboard the rowboat, and six puzzled pairs of Viking eyes were staring at the midget heroes. Then, with a shout, Olaf ordered his men, "Back to the galley. Old Rolf must see our strange catch!" Six oars soon pulled the boat to its parent ship, a small Viking galley. Then, cupped in Olaf's brown hands, Tom and Tink were carried aboard. A minute later the tiny pair were handed over to Rolf the Raider.

5 — Though his teeth were chattering with cold, Tom Thumb kept his voice steady as the bearded Viking chieftain lifted the midget adventurers up to eye-level. "Permit me, sir," he piped, sweeping off his hat, "to introduce Tom Thumb and Tinkel, two gentlemen adventurers from Merrie England!" A loud guffaw greeted the little hero's words. "O-ho!" roared Rolf. "I do not understand thee, little man, but thou are surely a better catch than two of the biggest whales in the Great Sea!"

6 — At that moment, a cry of alarm sounded from the bow of the galley. Tom and Tinkel were hurriedly put down as Rolf wheeled to see what was happening. As Tom clutched one of the main-mast stays, he gulped. A rakish-looking craft had appeared suddenly from behind a spur of the coastline, and was bearing down on them at speed. Too late, the Vikings saw their danger, and tried to alter course. Closer came the strange ship, till with a crash she hit the side of the Viking galley!

7 — Jutting from the strange craft's prow were three giant steel claws. As the two ships met, these claws bit deep into the Viking galley's side, locking both vessels together. The steel claws narrowly missed Tom and Tinkel, and the shock of the crash threw the little fellows head over heels into a heap of fishing nets on the galley's deck. Tom was quickly on his feet, however, with a hand on his sword. For on to the Viking galley rushed a boarding party of dark-skinned Moors, armed to the teeth.

8 — The Moors were fierce fighters. Tom Thumb had heard many tales of these dangerous pirates, for pirates they were — Moorish pirates whose ship had been blown far from its normal haunts by a great gale. Their leader, and the first man aboard the galley, was a fierce-looking cut-throat who had in place of his left hand, a fearsome steel hook. The suddenness of the Moorish attack had taken the Norsemen by surprise, and after a short fight they were disarmed and taken prisoner.

9 — From the shelter of the fishing nets, Tom and Tink watched in dismay as their Viking friends were marched off to the pirate galley. Then, to their horror, two of the Moors began to hack holes in the deck of the Viking galley. "They're sinking the ship!" gasped Tom. Even as he spoke, the last of the pirates leaped nimbly on to the prow of the pirate craft, which at once began to draw away. Tom and Tink were marooned — on a sinking ship!

10 — Water flowed steadily through the gashes in the Viking galley's timbers, and Tinkel's eyes grew bigger and bigger. "What are we going to do?" he gasped. Tom Thumb quickly drew his sword. He had spotted several cork floats tied to the fishing net on which the pair were standing. "Quick, Tinkel," he cried. "Help me cut this cork free!" A few slashes of the tiny weapon served to free the cork, as the galley gave a lurch and started to keel over.

11 — Next moment a sudden surge of water carried the two adventurers off, clinging to their cork. They were not a moment too soon. The Moorish galley was preparing to leave as Tinkel paddled the cork float alongside. Tom grabbed desperately for one of the oars. Followed by Tink, he shinned up towards the side of the pirate ship and through the rowlocks to safety.

12 — The Vikings were chained to the rowing benches. They were being used as galley slaves by the cunning Moors! "Come on, Tink!" cried Tom. "Rolf and his men need help!" Together the little fellows crept along the deck. Suddenly Tink gave a gasp of fear, and clutched Tom's arm. Reaching down towards them was the shining hook of the Moorish chief!

1 — Baruda, chief of the Moorish pirates who had captured Tom Thumb and Tinkel, along with their Viking friends, was a cruel man. He had chained the Vikings to the oars of his ships, but for Tom and Tink he had something worse in store. Holding the tiny fellows in his sharp hook, the one-armed Moor opened the parrot cage which hung from his cabin roof. "Little men," he mocked, "my parrot, Saladin, will tear you to shreds!"

2 — Tom and Tink fought to escape, but Baruda thrust them into the cage, where a fierce, red-coloured parrot swung on a perch. As the Moor locked the cage, there was a knock on the cabin door, and someone cried, "Come, Baruda! There is a ship in sight!" The pirate chief strode out of the cabin, snarling over his shoulder, "Soon you will perish, but, alas, I cannot stay to see Saladin at work!"

3 — The cabin door had scarcely closed before the red parrot swooped on Tom Thumb. Little Tom dodged the cruel beak by swarming up the bars of the cage. The parrot wheeled round on poor Tink, and caught him in its claws. Then Tom, leaning down, seized one of the bird's feathers and pulled with all his might. The parrot, screaming with pain, dropped Tink, who climbed swiftly up beside Tom. "Here, Tink!" cried Tom Thumb. "Help me to lift out the parrot's drinking jar!"

4 — Saladin, the parrot, was mad with rage, and Tom and Tink had to work fast to save their lives. Before the bird could attack again, the tiny comrades managed to lift the drinking jar from its holder. When the parrot flew at them, they were ready for it. "Now, Tink!" cried Tom. "Jump!" Holding the drinking jar between them, Tom and Tink leapt from the bars. Down came the jar, right over the parrot's head, and Tom and Tink soon jammed it on as hard as could be.

5 — While the parrot fluttered blindly round, Tom thought fast. "Listen, Tink," he said suddenly. "If we can make a fire, I know a way to get free. Hurry!" Tink knew what was needed. He found two chips of wood and a small piece of cord on the floor of the cage. One of the wooden slivers had a sharp point, and round it Tink twisted the cord. Then, with the pointed sliver biting into the other chip of wood, Tink and Tom Thumb managed to start a small flame.

6 — Now Tom Thumb kindled a small torch and clambered up to the roof of the cage. Then he set fire to the rope on which the cage was suspended. As the dry rope caught alight, some sparks crackled down into the cage. Saladin, the parrot, terrified by the smell of fire, dashed round more wildly than before, and the cage swung to and fro. Tom and Tink clung to the bars, watching the flames eat into the rope, and braced themselves for the fall that would come.

7 — Five seconds later, the cage came crashing down on the floor of the cabin, and what Tom Thumb had hoped for really happened. The heavy fall buckled the slender bars of the cage, and he and Tink were able to squeeze out. At last they were free — and now was the time to take revenge on Baruda the Moor, who had left them to die a terrible death.

8 — Tom's first move was to recover the sword which the Moor had taken from him. Next he climbed up to the cabin window, and glanced up at the great sail of the pirate ship. Then he scrambled down from the window, and ran to a box of fish-hooks which lay in a corner. "Take two hooks, and break the barbs off them," he said to Tink.

9 — Each carrying two barbless fish-hooks, Tom and Tink crept out of the open window of the cabin. Silently they made their way to a spot from which they could put Tom's daring plan into action. None of the pirates saw the two small figures leaping on to the bottom of the big sail. The Moors, gathered in the bows of the galley, were too busy watching the ship they meant to attack, or testing the edges of their curved swords.

10 — Up the great sail went Tom and Tink, hand over hand. The fish hooks, without their barbs, slipped easily in and out of the sail, but by the time Tom and Tink reached the top of the sail, the muscles of their little arms were aching with the strain. Tom Thumb peered down at the pirates on the deck below. Then he laughed quietly, and drew his trusty sword. "Baruda will pay for his misdeeds!" he chuckled.

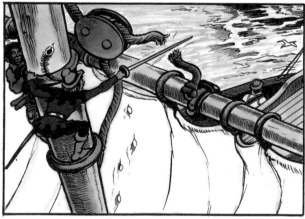

11 — Tom and Tink took it in turn to hack at the thick rope attached to the sail. That rope was used to lower or hoist the sail, and if it was cut the sail would fall. But the task of cutting the rope was a heavy one, for Tom's tiny sword was soon blunted on the tough fibres. And all the time the Moorish galley was closing in on its prey. Baruda kept lashing at the oarsmen, and crying out for more speed. The galley was close to the other ship when Tom Thumb slashed through the last strand of the rope that held the sail.

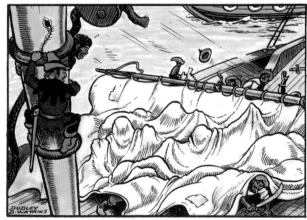

12 — The force of the wind carried the great sail forward towards the prow of the galley. Tom and Tink yelled in glee as they saw the pirates disappear under the canvas. The Moors were taken off their guard, and had no chance to dodge out of the way. Tom and Tink could hear their muffled yells as they struggled to wriggle from under the sail. "Now we must free the Vikings!" cried Tom Thumb. "Baruda has the keys at his belt. We will take them and unlock the rowing chains. Baruda and his Moorish dogs will scour the seas no more!"

1 — Aboard the galley of Baruda and his Moorish pirates, Tom Thumb and Tinkel, the black boy, had done a clever thing. The brave little chaps had hacked down the galley's sail, and sent it hurtling down over the heads of the pirates just as they were ready to attack another ship. Now Tom and Tink slid quickly to the deck. "Baruda lies yonder!" cried Tom, pointing to the bows of the ship. "We must get the keys he carries!"

2 — Most of the Moorish pirates were struggling to free themselves from the folds of the sail, but the one-armed Baruda had been stunned by the heavy wooden boom on which the sail was spread. Tom and Tink were soon at his side, and it did not take them long to cut the key-ring from the pirate's belt. The little fellows knew that *one* of the keys on the ring could free their Viking friends who were chained to the oars of the galley.

3 — The Vikings sat at the rowing benches, still pulling on the oars. They had their backs to the prow of the ship, and so they did not know that the great sail had fallen on the Moors. Nor did they notice the tiny figures of Tom and Tink running to the lock that held the end of the rowing chains. Tom Thumb soon found which key was needed, and he and Tink quickly opened the lock.

4 — Not until Tom climbed up beside old Rolf the Raider and pointed to the loose end of the chain did the Viking know he was free. Rolf gave a loud yell of joy. "Come, men!" he cried to his companions at the oars. "We are free!" Tom and Tink did not understand Rolf's language, but they jumped for joy as the Viking chief made straight for the place where the Moors kept their spare weapons.

5 — Rolf the Raider and his men armed themselves and raced forward to attack the Moorish pirates, who were creeping from under the sail. Tom Thumb and Tink scrambled up on to the sail of the ship. "Look, Tom!" gasped Tink, suddenly. "That cruel Baruda — he is getting up!" Tink was right. The pirate chief had opened his eyes. He had seen the Vikings rushing to the attack, and had drawn his sword ready to meet them. Tom Thumb knew how Baruda could fight with that big, curved sword, and he glanced round for a way to stop the pirate.

6 — Tom Thumb acted like lightning. On the other side of the galley was a great block through which a rope ran to brace the mast. The rope which held the block to the side of the galley was half rotten. Tom whipped out his little sword and slashed at the rope. A few blows cut through the strands, just as Baruda, scimitar in hand, came bounding across the deck. The heavy block swished through the air. It hit the pirate full on the head, and sent him sprawling on the deck. With Baruda out of the fight, the Vikings soon overcame the rest of the pirates.

7 — Rolf the Raider ordered his men to chain the Moors to the rowing benches. But for the pirate chief he had a different plan. When Baruda recovered his senses, Rolf forced the pirate to climb into a barrel. "Ho, ho, ho!" cried Tom Thumb, guessing what Rolf meant to do. "Baruda will look funny." And when Olaf the Whaler cut a hole in the lid of the barrel, Baruda scowled and muttered angrily. But no one paid any attention to him, and the lid was nailed down so that only his head stuck out of the barrel.

8 — Rolf the Raider was proud of his tiny friends. He could not speak their language, and they could not speak his, but all three could "talk" by making signs. When the Vikings had hoisted the big sail once more, and headed the galley towards the north, Tom and Tink tried to tell old Rolf that they would like him to make a little ship for them. The big Viking understood. He got a block of wood, and began to carve a model Viking galley. From behind Baruda's barrel, two beady eyes were watching. Baruda's parrot, Salinda, was still free!

9 — By the next afternoon, old Rolf had finished the model galley, and he presented it to Tom and Tink. But the little chaps no sooner had their galley than they wanted to sail in it. When Rolf saw what they wanted, he laughed and nodded. Then he ordered one of the Vikings to launch the little ship. When this had been done, Tom and Tink were delighted.

10 — The tiny galley, towed on a long cord, bobbed over the waves just like a real Viking war ship. Tom and Tink were so happy with their new toy that they did not see Saladin, the red parrot, flutter on to the side of the pirate ship. Baruda had been whispering to the cunning bird when none of the Vikings could see, and now he had given Saladin an order.

11 — The big, red parrot was as cruel and clever as its one-armed master. Perched on the side of the ship, it peered at the little boat in which Tom Thumb and Tinkel were being towed. Then the parrot opened its wings. Silent as an owl, it flew to the tow line. Its sharp beak closed on the cord, and cut clean through it. Tom Thumb and Tink were adrift!

12 — It was a few minutes before Tom and Tink realised that they were no longer being towed. By then the pirate ship was some distance away. None of the Vikings had seen Saladin cut the rope. Tink shouted as loud as he could, but the pirate galley sailed on, drawing farther and farther away. Then Tom gave a cry of dismay. "Ice! Tink! Icebergs all around us!"

These excerpts were taken from BEANOS dated 19th April through to May 31st 1947.

DEAR DENNIS

BEANO readers send their hero **Dennis The Menace** thousands of letters each year. Here's a small selection, plus a few that were addressed to **Gnasher**, his fangtastic hound, and softy Walter, the boy **Dennis** reckons is wetter than Niagara Falls.

POST!

POST OFFICE

Dear Dennis,
I am getting very angry because none of my letters have been published. I am beginning to turn into a Softy!
Robert Parr,
Hornchurch, Essex.

Dear Robert,
Don't worry! You're not turning into a Softy. Softies do NOT become angry — they only become slightly annoyed, so if you were angry you aren't a Softy!
Yours menacingly,
Dennis.

Dear Gnasher,
Have you ever lost any teeth in a fight with a police dog?
Michael Smart,
Swavesey, Cambridgeshire.

Dear Michael,
In a fight with a police dog I have lost a few tufts of hair, bits of an ear, my temper, my freedom — but teeth? NEVER!
Yours fangly,
Gnasher.

Dear Dennis,
Why do you wear short trousers? I thought only Softies wore them.
Martin Rawson,
Corby, Northants.

Dear Martin,
My face strikes terror into the hearts of all Softies — and I've also got the fiercest-looking knees in the business, so why cover them up?
Yours shortly,
Dennis.

Dear Dennis and Gnasher,
I have a serious problem. I took in a seven-toed cat a year ago when he was a kitten. With all those extra claws I thought he'd grow up to be really dangerous, so I called him Slasher. Unfortunately, he's turned into a SOFTY! He won't fight at all, not even with dogs. What can I do?
Bella Melville,
Swansea.

Dear Bella,
Your cat's not a Softy. All he needs are some weapons to fight with. Train him to use a CATapult!
Yours daftly,
Dennis and Gnasher.

Dear Dennis the Menace,
Have you ever had an attendance prize at school?
Tina Wood,
Sale, Cheshire.

Dear Tina,
I once had a perfect attendance record — at the Head's room for extra-punishment every day for a term.
Yours punctually,
Dennis.

Dear Gnasher,
I have been reading about prehistoric monsters and I am wondering if your ancestors were woolly mammoths? I think "The Beano" is the best comic.
Steven Kay,
Carnoustie, Tayside.

Dear Steven,
I believe I'm descended from the Sabre-toothed Gnashtiger — and I wish I was back in these good old days. A 20 ft.-long dinosaur bone would have made a lovely snack.
Yours chewly,
Gnasher.

Dear Walter,
Why don't you get your own back on Dennis? Buy some stink bombs, put a clothes peg on your nose, then throw them into Dennis's den.
Lori Savage,
Folkestone, Kent.

Dear Lori,
That's a most adventurous plan — even slightly dangerous (brave titter). But there is a serious drawback — a clothes peg would be awfully sore on my extremely delicate nostrils.
Yours very softly,
Walter.

Dear Gnasher,
My dog is frightened of worms. Could you please help me?
Julian Hamilton,
Bierton, Bucks.

Dear Julian,
Frightened of worms? How low can you get? I suggest you teach him to beat up a tin of spaghetti. This may help to boost his confidence.
Helpfully yours,
Gnasher.

Dear Dennis,
Have you ever thought of entering Gnasher for "Crufts"?
Lynne Bellamy,
Broadstairs, Kent.

Dear Lynne,
I once entered Gnasher for the local Dog Show and he won a "Highly Condemned"!
Your chum, Dennis.

Dear Dennis,
Why don't you start your own water works factory with all the tears that come out of Walter's eyes? You would make a fortune. If you do do it, I hope you do well.
Sandra Biagioni,
Ayr, Scotland.

Dear Sandra,
Good idea! We could call it the WALTER WORKS.
Your chum,
Dennis.

Dear Gnasher,
Every time I see my goldfish he is getting smaller. What should I do?
Craig Alcock,
Wyken, Coventry.

Dear Craig,
It sounds to me as if the water in the bowl is making him shrink!
Your puzzled pup,
Gnasher.

Dear Dennis,
Because I have read so much about you I have awarded myself a Professorship of Menaceology, and, as such, I wish to give an honorary degree to you, Dennis, for being the greatest bad egg and one for Gnasher for terrifying Walter.
Damian McGrath,
Crewe, Cheshire.

Dear Professor,
Thank you very much. How about awarding Walter something too — a plateful of soggy custard over his soppy head?
Yours proudly,
Dennis and Gnasher.

Dear Gnasher,
How many pieces of Walter's trousers have you got, and where do you keep them?
Andrew Stuffs,
Newcastle under Lyme, Staffs.

Dear Andrew,
I've twenty-two pieces gnashed from Walter's trousers and Dennis has promised to make a patch-work quilt with them for my sleeping-basket. He says he'll need many more than twenty-two pieces, so I'm going to lie in wait for the postman, the coalman, the milkman and our local bobby.
Yours rippingly,
Gnasher.

Dennis and **Gnasher** are modelling the stylish T-shirts that lucky letter writers receive as prizes.

MENACES FOR EVER

BATTLING FOR BRITAIN

During those dark days of World War II, nowhere was more patriotic than the pages of DANDY and BEANO, where **Lord Snooty, Desperate Dan** and Co. were determined to do their bit for their country.

The comic superstars' main contribution to the war effort was to put a smile on the faces of the nation, even when those faces were often hidden behind gas masks.

Paper shortages may have forced BEANO and DANDY to appear fortnightly, but nothing could diminish the comics' patriotic fervour.

LORD SNOOTY'S RAW RECRUITS

Lord Snooty and his pals were quick to sign up anyone for the war effort who could throw a spanner into Hitler's works. And as you can see from these two 1940 adventures, those recruits included some very unlikely characters.

WAR IN THE AIR

Podge, the rotund superstar of DANDY'S early years, must have been one of the very few Britons ever to cheer a German air raid.

Freddy The Fearless Fly, above, and **Desperate Dan** on the facing page, proved there was more than one way to bring down a Nazi plane.

MEET MUSSO

BEANO readers, too young to see front line action themselves, were treated to the spectacle of Italian leader **Mussolini's** regular humiliation in their favourite comic.

With friends like Hitler, who needed enemies? But whether **Musso** needed enemies or not, he had millions of them — the readers of BEANO, as the two strips below illustrate.

And when **Musso** met three great British legends — **John Bull, Winston Churchill** and **Pansy Potter,** the end results were never in doubt, as you can see on the opposite page.

ADDIE AND HERMY

Readers of wartime issues of DANDY didn't need a crystal ball to know what the future held in store for Adolf Hitler, the German leader, and his sidekick Herman Goering.

By Request

FOOD GLORIOUS FOOD

The two wartime obsessions of food shortages and a desire to see the Nazis come unstuck were combined in these **Addie and Hermy** strips.

CALL TO ARMS (AND PAWS)

Believe it or not, even Britain's most famous cat heeded the recruiting sergeant's call, and it wasn't only his own neck **Korky** stuck out for Britain.

Shucks! If a pesky cat could join up, there had to be a place in the forces for the toughest guy in comics. And there was! **Desperate Dan** became Able Seaman Dan in the wartime adventure, overleaf!

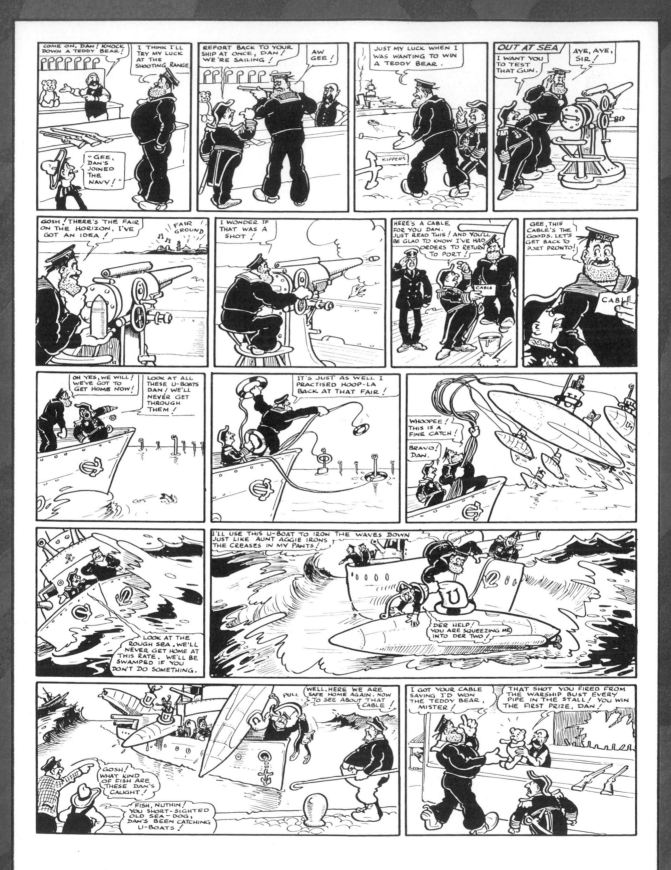

When you see the combined might of The Allies (we mean DANDY and BEANO) it's no surprise that Hitler and his mates were sent packing. The two comics were certainly . . .

BATTLING FOR BRITAIN!

"THANKS A MILLION, DOCTOR DENNIS!"

DENNIS THE MEDICINE — WILL GNURSE YOU BACK TO HEALTH.

That was the message the world's biggest menace received from BEANO fanatic, Tim Wilson, of Harrogate. And the reason for this praise? The Yorkshire lad reckoned that **Dennis** had saved his life.

When Tim was holidaying in Spain he was the victim of a swimming accident and pronounced clinically dead. The youngster's parents played Tim non-stop tapes of **Dennis** stories during his 48-hour coma until he pulled through, and now Tim's back to normal and his menacing pranks are second only to his hero's.

And as if that wasn't happy ending enough, when BEANO editor Euan Kerr heard the tale, he hot-footed it down to Yorkshire to present Tim with a souvenir framed cartoon featuring **Dennis, Tim** and **Gnasher.**

WE'RE ON THE RADIO

Radio 1 D.J. Steve Wright left his listeners in no doubt that he was a BEANO fan, so the BEANO editor reckoned it was only fair to let his readers know that he was an admirer of Steve's. And how better, than to feature Steve's crazy sidekick Mr Mad in the comic.

When it came to depicting this weird character who lives in a rubbish skip, Mr Mad obliged by personally providing a picture of himself for the BEANO artist to copy.

When DANDY celebrated its 50th birthday there was no shortage of celebrities offering congratulations, including many TV and radio stars. Britain's oldest comic was delighted to receive birthday greetings from two of the biggest names on radio.

Derek Jameson contacted DANDY and chatted to the staff during his popular breakfast show. Derek had fond memories of **Desperate Dan,** and quipped, "We loved 'im then and we still love 'im!"

During his Saturday morning show on Radio 2, Michael Aspel took time off from interviewing singer Elaine Paige to chat with the DANDY staff on the air. Michael wondered how **Dan** was bearing up after 50 years of comic stardom and was pleased to be told that the big guy had never felt better.

This is how Mr Mad appeared in BEANO dated 30th January 1988.

SCHEMERS AND DODGERS

If there was a hall of fame for slippery guys and dodgy characters, there's no doubt that top TV schemers, Sergeant Bilko and Arthur Daley, would be given pride of place. And every comic reader knows who'd be that hall of fame's first two junior members . . . **Winker Watson,** Dandy's wily wangler and **Roger,** Beano's biggest dodger.

If **Roger** had spent as much time studying as he has devising schemes to avoid homework he'd probably be a professor by now. Here's a typical **Roger** masterplan from 1st August, 1964. And on 20th May, 1961, **Winker Watson** pitted his wits against Mr Creep, his long-suffering teacher. The story appears overleaf.

A VERY COMIC CHRISTMAS

During the last fifty years there have been quite a few changes in DANDY and BEANO, but one thing has certainly remained the same, and that's the way the two comics celebrate Christmas . . . in a **BIG** way!

DANDY BEANO

SPECIAL DELIVERY SERVICE

If DANDY and BEANO had arrived on the scene much later, they'd have missed the 1930s altogether. DANDY'S debut was on 4th December, 1937, making the comic a mere four issues old when its first festive number appeared.

Korky's Christmas caper below is from 1939, while on the opposite page, **Big Eggo** was the cover star in BEANO'S first Christmas issue.

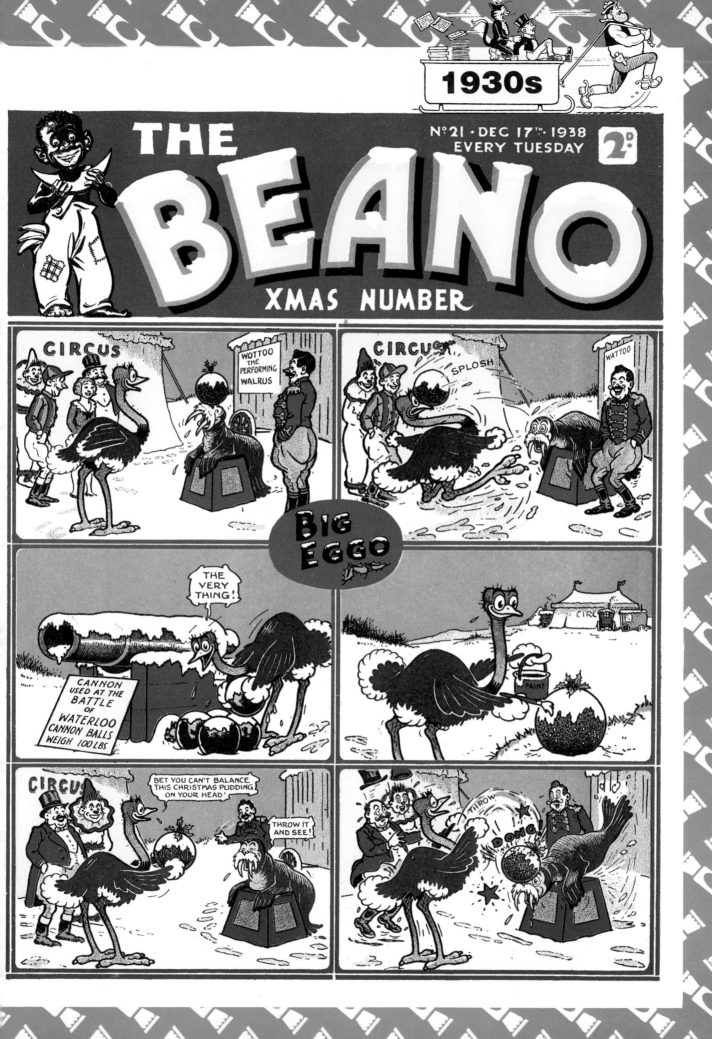

CHRISTMAS AT BUNKERTON CASTLE

In **Lord Snooty's** ancestral home, Christmas wasn't a time for goodwill towards ALL men, as a glance at the castle footmen will confirm.

LORD SNOOTY from BEANO, Christmas 1942.

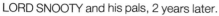

LORD SNOOTY and his pals, 2 years later.

A PAIR OF DUFFERS

There's only one day a year when that phrase could possibly describe **Korky** and **Desperate Dan**, and that's Christmas Day.

The two comic superstars with plum duffs in tow (or in tum), have been regular festive sights for the last half century.

The **Korky** story below is from 1946, but we wouldn't advise our young readers to copy his cycling style on Christmas Day, or any other day. Cats may have nine lives, but children don't.

No-one can say that **Desperate Dan** stories aren't educational. After reading this 1947 story, readers knew the difference between a Christmas cow-pie and an ordinary one — the Christmas variety doesn't have horns.

GIFTS GALORE

1950s

When it comes to Christmas presents, BEANO funny girls, **Pansy Potter** and **Minnie The Minx,** have received their share, and given their readers lots of laughs in return.

Santa's sack socked **Pansy Potter**, below, in 1952 and **Minnie The Minx** met the military in the festive tale, opposite, five years later.

WHAT'S THE BEST BIRD FOR CHRISTMAS?

Chicken? Turkey? If you'd asked BEANO readers that question in the 1950s, they'd have answered — canary, or more accurately — **Kanary**, because when that tiny ball of fun and feathers gave big bad **Kat** a hard time, it meant Christmas cackles galore.

The battle below first appeared in 1953.

HAVING A SMASHING CHRISTMAS

When DANDY'S **Smasher** celebrated the festive season in 1959, it wasn't so much a case of stockings round the Christmas tree, as socks on the nose. It was appropriate that this particular story appeared in the issue dated 26th December — Boxing Day!

And if you're wondering whether those Santas turned blue with cold, it's simply that DANDY'S back page of that era was only printed in blue and yellow.

PARTY TIME

In the pages of BEANO, bears and Red Injuns are usually found feuding, but Christmas is a time to bury the peace pipe and smoke the hatchet (they don't do things by the book in BEANO). Old differences were forgotten in this **Three Bears** story from 1960, while everyone enjoyed a Christmas bash of the non-violent variety. And when it comes to bashes, where better to find one than **Bash Street**? The party on the right took place in 1961.

It was always a White Christmas for this particular DANDY star — **JOE WHITE!** And when Joe was around, his seven little pals were never far away as you can see in this story from 1963.

PUTTING CHRISTMAS ON THE COVER

. . . That was **Biffo's** yuletide task in BEANO for more than two decades. Here's just a few of those festive funnies including a Christmas quiz. Test your knowledge of BEANO circa 1969. The answers are below.

BULLY FOR CHRISTMAS

As far as DANDY readers are concerned, you can forget the turkey and stuffing with cranberry sauce or even the plum duff, but no Christmas feast of fun would be complete without . . . **BULLY BEEF AND CHIPS.**

Christmas is a time for giving and Bully Beef goes along with that. He never lets a festive season pass without giving something to his little 'pal' Chips, things like . . . bashes, bruises, black eyes and a bad time! But don't worry. Chips always gets something sweet at Christmas . . . SWEET REVENGE!

If you thought you'd never see the **Bash Street Kids** rushing into school, you're wrong! There was one occasion, Christmas, 1971, when they couldn't wait to dash inside. Here's why . . .

HAVING A MIGHTY FINE CHRISTMAS! (WITH

It doesn't seem to matter what time of year it is, **Desperate Dan's** strength is as great as ever. Unfortunately, so is his clumsiness, and his ability to cause a disaster even when he's only trying to introduce a little Christmas cheer.

When **Dennis** is around, his faithful pets, **Rasher** and **Gnasher** are never far behind — and in **Gnasher's** case, never far from a behind. He loves gnashing posties' pants.

Here's festive farmyard fun with **Rasher** from 1984 and tree-mendous Christmas cackles, Gnasher-style, from the previous year.

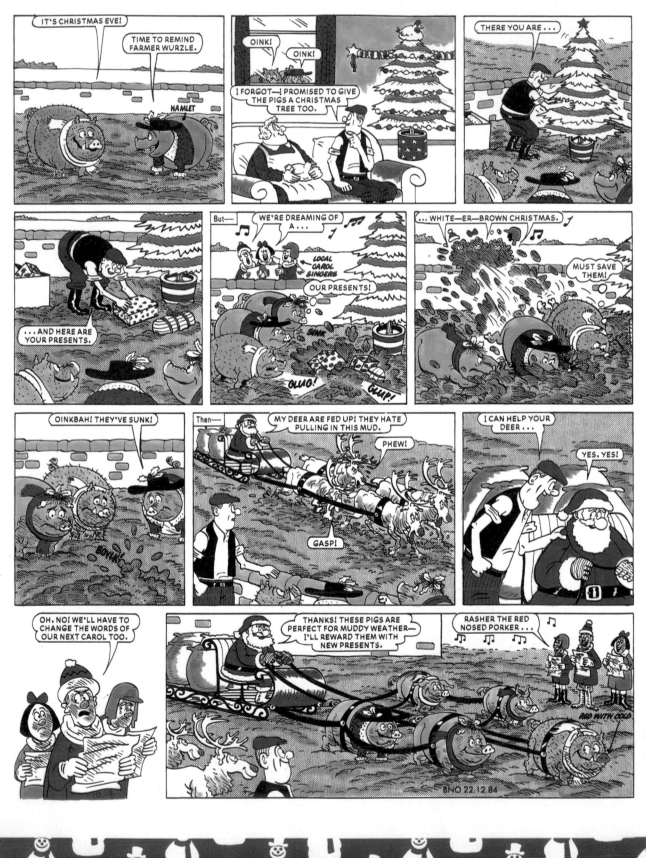

There's only one way to follow **A Very Comic Christmas,** and that's with a . . .

...HA-HA- HAPPY N[

A **Korky** story always has lots of hoots in it, but in 1955 it was "Hoots, Mon!" as the feline superstar played out the old year with a set of decidedly home-made bagpipes.

Saying goodbye to 1951 didn't prove such an easy task for BEANO strong-girl **Pansy Potter.** If it hadn't been for Pansy's prompt action, December 32nd would have been added to the calendar.

SOMETHING FOR NOTHING

DANDY and BEANO's reputation for generosity dates back over 50 years to the comics' first issues. When DANDY was launched, every reader received a free whistle, and each copy of BEANO number one contained a gift of a mask.

A fondly remembered gift from the early days was the tin jumping frog in the second issue of DANDY.

Not every reader is lucky enough to have one of these on their bedroom wall. The comics' editors had limited numbers of these special posters printed, to give away as prizes.

This colourful selection of gifts is only a few of the wide range of novelties and sweets that the two comics have given away over the years.

Here's a riddle — DANDY and BEANO have given away hundreds of them, but not to their readers. What are they?

The answer is **press kits**.

These glossy folders, packed with facts, figures and fun were sent out to newspapers, TV companies and radio stations, letting them know about DANDY and BEANO's 50th birthdays.

And here's what loyal readers did receive . . . two giant, double-sided posters celebrating the comics' first half centuries.

GREAT MOMENTS IN HISTORY

When that cute bear **Biffo** made his BEANO debut in 1948, who could have guessed that he'd remain the comic's cover star until 1974.

The stars of BEANO have always been ready to party, and what better excuse for a knees-up than their 25th birthday on 27th July, 1963.

BEANO'S SEASIDE SNAPS

BEANO has been Britain's biggest-selling comic for decades but on 16th June, 1988, it became the biggest comic in a totally different way.

As part of Scarborough's Visual Arts Extravaganza, a team of 100 schoolchildren led by festival director David Hann, modelled that week's BEANO cover into a giant beach sculpture, a record-beating 150 feet by 250 feet in size.

As the photographs of the great event show, it was an amazing sight . . . until the tide came in.

By Request

For more than fifty years, DANDY and BEANO readers have been entertained by animals' antics. The comics' very first cover stars were **Korky The Cat** and **Big Eggo,** the ostrich. In fact DANDY and BEANO have featured . . .

... ALL CREATURES GREAT AND SMALL ...

...PLUS A FEW HAIRY, SCARY, FIERCE AND FURRY ONES!

WHAT A KAT-ASTROPHE

Every time **Kat** met **Kanary** it ended in tears — for the big guy. During the 50s, this ferocious feline and his feathered "friend" battled it out with brains consistently beating brawn.

Kanary led **Kat** a dog's life in this story from Beano dated 6th February, 1954 and **Kat** threw a party with **cat**astrophic results on 27th March of the same year.

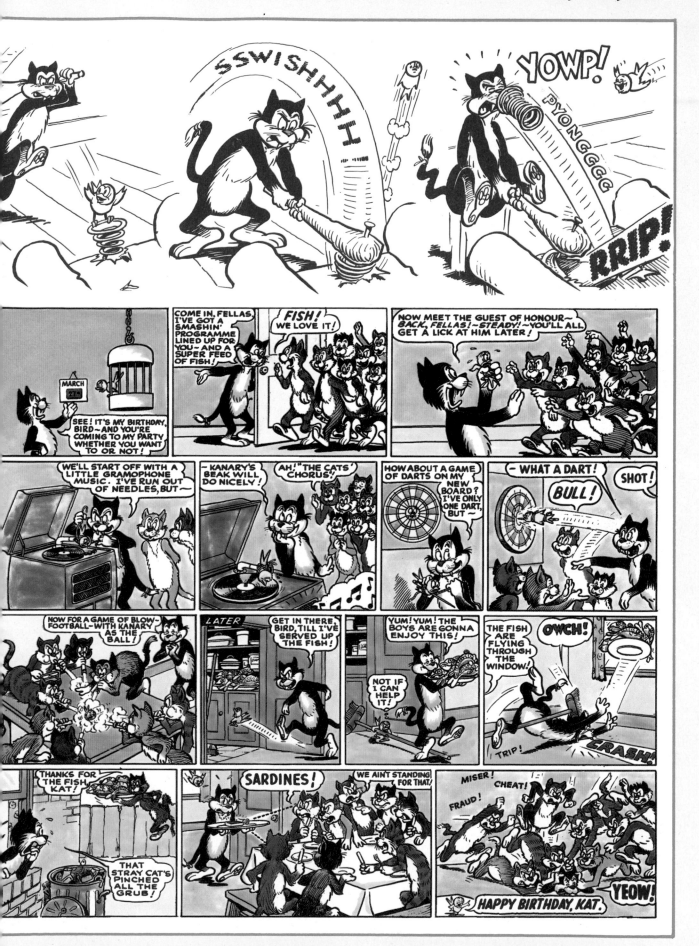

But the guide knew better. He didn't believe in the ghosts he talked about. It was Scamper he spotted. Fancy that hairy horror sneaking in against his orders!

IT'S THAT GIANT SPIDER!

YOWCH!

I'M OFF!

Out of the bed sprang the horrified diamond thief. He pelted outside, while Old Whiskers chased Scamper with an outsize battleaxe.

GET OUT OF HERE!

To avoid being pinned like a butterfly, Spunky's Spider took a daring leap into the moat, just missing a last thrust from the guide's axe.

AND DON'T COME BACK!

At a nearby stream, Scamper borrowed a fish-hook from little Alf Rugg. He knew Hot-Ice Harry was up to no good, and there might be a use for that hook.

SURE, YOU CAN HAVE IT, SCAMPER!

Sure enough, out of a window came Hot-Ice Harry with the coronet.

THIS IS DEAD EASY!

YOW! SOMETHING STUNG ME!

Scamper had slung his hook and scored a hit on the seat of Harry's trousers!

The thief was helpless. Scamper's steady pull was dragging him off the wall—and Scamper's line was made of super-strong spider-thread!

LOOK! HE'S GOT THE DUKE'S CORONET!

GOOD FOR YOU, SCAMPER!

HE'S HOOKED!

HELP!

From a tower window, Spunky and Old Whiskers saw the downfall of the diamond thief. With a cry of despair, he lost his grip and went tumbling towards the slimy waters of the moat.

Splash! Hot-Ice shivered and gulped cold water. He might have drowned if Scamper hadn't kept hold of his line and pulled him to the bank like a sardine looking for a slice of toast to sit on.

SPLUTTER-SPLUTTER!

Spunky took charge of Harry the thief, tying him up with Scamper's special spider thread till the policeman arrived, while Old Whiskers proudly told the noble Duke of Crumbleigh that a boy and his pet spider had saved the precious coronet.

WHAT'S BEEN GOING ON HERE?

Was the Duke delighted? Indeed, he was! Seated in his ducal living-room, where the roaring fire burnt two whole trees every day, he ordered cake and cocoa for Spunky and his Spider. The Noble Duke was a noble host, and Spunky ate up nobly. But he couldn't keep pace with the appetite of his pet spider!

CAN MY PET HAVE TWO PIECES OF CAKE, MR DUKE, SIR?

SURE, SON! HE EARNED THEM!

BEASTLY DENNIS

Back in the BEANO of the 1950s no one could accuse **Dennis The Menace** of being a softy where animals were concerned. The bigger the beast, the better Dennis liked it! Well, until the final frames of each story, at least.

DANDY and BEANO readers know there's always fun in store when they turn to an animal story. Never more so than when **Charlie the Chimp** ran amok in a department store in the 1958 Dandy Annual.

DANDY'S **Dirty Dick** knew exactly where to find all creatures great and small — his local zoo! And it took **Dick** no time to meet up with one that was grubby and grotty as well!

By Request

DEAR DAN

SHUCKS! YOU FOLKS OUT THERE SEND ME A MIGHTY LOT OF LETTERS! HERE'S JUST A FEW THAT MADE ME CHUCKLE!

DESPERATELY calling Desperate Dan!

We are chefs on board H.M.S. Newcastle, serving in the South Atlantic (again).

Please send us your muscle building exercises as we're getting a bit fat — we're eating too many of our own cow-pies!

Once the rest of the ship's company know we are DAN FANS — there will be no more complaints about our cooking!
— **The Chefs, 2QZ Mess, H.M.S. Newcastle.**
DAN says —

Anyone who complains about my cow-pies should be made to walk the plank.

ONE day my little sister rolled up her sleeve and said she had strong "cockles". Of course she meant muscles, but I couldn't show her my stronger muscles because I was laughing so much.
— **Jim McBride, Paisley.**
DAN says —

Showing off my muscles has cost me a fortune. Every time I flex 'em I rip my shirt!

AFTER making a see-saw with my sister, I felt very hungry, so I went and bought a strawberry pie.

I put it down on the see-saw for a moment. What a blunder! My sister tripped over her shoe-lace, fell on the see-saw — and the pie went up in the air and landed on her head!

Mum was furious!
— **Amar Majid, Liversedge, W. Yorkshire.**
DAN says —

Chuckle! Sounds like pie in the sky to me!

WHEN my sister's friend came for tea, we had a bottle of ketchup on the table. After using some I put the top back on, or so I thought.

My sister's friend picked up the bottle but it slipped out of her fingers and the sauce poured out, all over the cat who happened to be walking past. That was a laugh!
— **Denise Meakin, Warmington, Cheshire.**
DAN says —

I prefer putting ketchup on dogs . . . hot dogs, that is!

AT breakfast one morning, I put a ping-pong ball, painted red, on my Dad's plate.

He thought it was a tomato. What a shock he got when he tried to stick his fork into it!
— **Darren Parish, Driffield, Yorkshire.**
DAN says —
That reminds me of the time I played table tennis with a rotten egg. First it went "Ping" then "PONG"!

WHEN a herd of cattle was being driven through our town, a big bull wandered into our garden and then began knocking on the window with the ring on its nose.

My Mum screamed and ran upstairs, but I was so young that I didn't realise it was dangerous. I banged on the window and the bull took to its heels and fled.

Mum thought I was a hero.
Dara McClatchie, Co. Dublin.,
DAN says —
I'm surprised you weren't re-named Desperate Dara.

AT tea-time one day, I dug up some worms from the garden and put them in a bowl, mixed with some tomato sauce and gave them to my sister.

She asked me what it was meant to be. I said, "Wormghetti".

She looked at the plate, saw the worms moving and screamed.

She's never eaten spaghetti since.
— **Ferga Brogan, Ballymena, Co. Antrim.**
DAN says —
Wonder if the worms liked the taste of tomato sauce?

AM I your farthest away reader? I live in Medicine Hat, Alberta, Canada and I am a cowboy too, Dan.

We live out in the prairie where the deer and the antelope play. We can see them when we look out of our back window.

My Gran sends me The DANDY every week.
— **Russel Bradbury, Medicine Hat, Alberta.**
DAN says —
Howdy, partner! See any cowboys out there? You'll recognise them this way. When a cowboy gets hungry he goes for his buns!

THE funniest food I've ever tasted was when I was on a battle camp with my Dad. The Gurkha soldiers brought in a pot filled to the brim with curry.

When I was offered some, I gladly took a huge bowlful, as I was starving. I scoffed the lot, then I asked what it was.

"Hornet curry," was the reply. They had found a nest of hornets, sprayed them with fly spray, caught the insects, then deep fried them until they were crispy.

From now on, no matter how hungry I am, I always find out what I'm about to eat.
— **Steven Jeffery, B.F.P.O. 1.**
DAN says —
Guess that curry had a sting in it!

I PLAYED a great trick on my sister. She uses a yellow-coloured hair conditioner, so I sneaked it away and emptied out the contents. Then I filled the bottle up with the yolks of five bad eggs.

When my sister used it she said, "Phew, what a smell."

Then she came out of the bathroom with egg yolk running down her face. No one would go near her for ages because of the horrible "eggy" smell.
— **Graham Hall, Garston, Herts.**
DAN says —
Sounds like a real sham"POO", Graham.

THE other day my Dad asked, "What's good to eat and bends iron bars?"

"I don't know," I replied.

So he said, "Desperate Flan!"
— **Myles Duckworth, Whalley, Lancs.**
DAN says —
Ho-ho! Sounds like the stuff Katey brought home from her first cookery lesson. It was tough as concrete and would have bent iron bars, too!

THE other week I went to my uncle's farm. He asked me to help him feed the animals.

I was surprised when I found he gave them cow-pie!

Please could you send a T-shirt, not for me, but for my uncle's Desperate Pig!
— **Mark Dowell, Brighouse, Yorks.**
DAN says —
If your uncle's pig receives a T-shirt, he'll "hog" the limelight.

THE biggest meal I ever had was a full-sized adult portion of Chinese Beef Chop Suey followed by a helping of pineapple and ice cream.

Do you like Chinese food, Dan?
— **Alex Shepherd, Abbots, Bromley.**
DAN says —
I like any kind of grub, but I don't like these spindly chopsticks you get in Chinese restaurants. I use clothes pole chopsticks to get proper Dan-sized helpings.

KEEP 'EM COMIN'! I NEVER GET TIRED OF READIN' YOUR LETTERS!

DANDY'S RIPPING YARNS

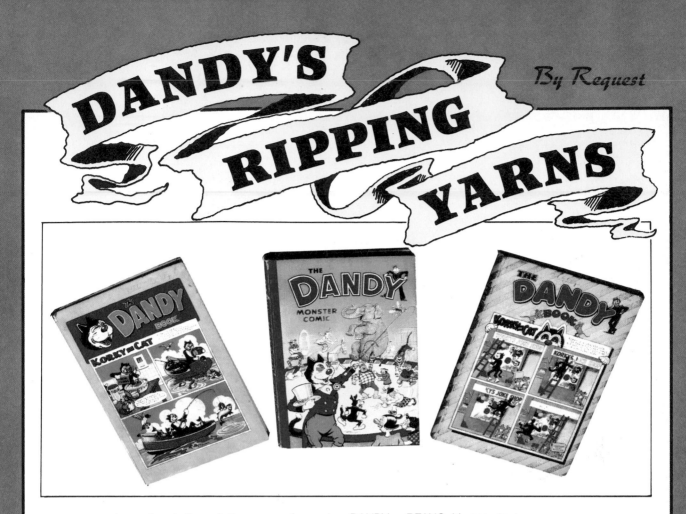

As we thumb through the pages of a modern DANDY or BEANO, it's easy to forget what a large role adventure stories played in the comics' early years. Both weekly issues and annuals carried these thrilling tales. But they haven't completely disappeared. One can still be found each year in the Dandy Annual.

The riotous scene below is from **Mickey's Tick Tock Men,** a story in the 1956 Dandy Book, and the classic yarn, which begins overleaf, first appeared in the 1951 Annual.

BRAVE YOUNG BLACK-HOOF

YOUNG Chief Hawkeye of the Blackfeet Indian tribe let his magnificent colt, Black-Hoof, pick his steps among the slippery rocks on the shore of Thunder River, for the boy Chief had a tricky job in hand. He was trying to rope a horse, which stood in a canoe floating rapidly down the river to Bison Falls. The horse was alone, and bore two bags filled with strange articles. The lariat's loop left Hawkeye's hand and sped towards its target.

2 — Right on the brink of the falls, the runaway canoe was halted. Hawkeye's lasso settled round the horse's neck, and the animal braced its legs against the canoe's sides to resist the pull of the rope. But gradually the combined strength of the young Indian and his sturdy colt dragged both horse and canoe closer. Then, dismounting, Hawkeye stretched his arm to grab the reins of the pack-horse, while Black-Hoof climbed the steep bank.

3 — Guided by Hawkeye, and assisted by the intelligent Black-Hoof taking the strain on the rope, the laden horse managed to leap from the canoe to a rock on the river-bank. At once the canoe plunged over the brink of the fall, to be smashed to matchwood in the whirlpool below. "Well done, my little wild colt!" said Hawkeye to the panting Black-Hoof. He calmed the pack-horse and had a look at the queer articles in its load. They were children's toys.

4 — "This is a white man's horse," said Hawkeye to one of his warriors when he arrived home at his Blackfeet village. "See, its coat is trimmed. Its hoofs are shod with the white iron. Guard it well while I consult with the elders." But there was an excited gleam in the eyes of Strongarm, the painted brave whom he left to guard the horse. Strongarm was very curious about the strange goods in those bags, and in two minutes he had tumbled everything out.

5 — More warriors joined Strongarm. Like children they stared at dolls, drums, trumpets, a scooter, a rocking-horse, and many more Paleface toys. Like children those big husky braves played with the toys, and the little Indian youngsters who came near were thrust aside. Strongarm admired a flaxen-haired, blue-eyed doll. "Paleface goddess," he grunted, stroking its wax cheeks. And then Hawkeye returned, and what he saw made him very angry.

6 — "Are my warriors papooses — that they play with toys like Paleface babes!" he cried roughly. "Put these playthings back where they came from. The elders say we must keep the white man's goods till he who owns them comes to claim them." Ashamed, most of the warriors replaced the toys in the saddle-bags. But not Strongarm. He drew his tomahawk. "Who steals my Paleface goddess dies!" he snarled. Mounting his pony, he rode madly away.

7 — Hawkeye's face darkened with rage. At his urgent whistle, Black-Hoof bounded towards him, and he rode in pursuit of the reckless warrior. Strongarm's pony was no match for the wild colt. After a mile or two, the warrior left his spent beast and climbed a rocky hill. There, on a ledge outside a cave, he took his stand against his chief. But there was a shock in store for both Strongarm and Hawkeye, for an awakened grizzly bear came out of the cave!

8 — Strongarm heard the menacing growl of the disturbed grizzly behind him. Casting aside his Paleface goddess, the warrior leapt from the rock-ledge just as the great beast charged. But Hawkeye was right in its path! Hastily he fired an arrow and tried to step aside. His foot slipped on a mossy rock, and down he went, while the monstrous bear, stung but not stopped by the bite of the arrow in its shoulder, threw its lumbering weight on top of the boy.

9 — Meanwhile, the ever-faithful Black-Hoof had followed his young master up the hill, and he arrived on the scene just as Hawkeye fell below the bear. Squirming and wriggling to avoid the brute's terrible claws, Hawkeye threw away his bow and felt for his knife. He was fighting for his life, rolling and twisting so that the grizzly couldn't hug him tight and squeeze the breath from his body. Then Black-Hoof, venting his anger in a shrill neigh, dashed to the rescue.

10 — Black-Hoof saw his chance as the bear rose on its hind legs to get a better look at its squirming victim. His hard hooves shot out with terrific force in a back-kick that pounded the breath out of the grizzly in a snorting gasp. Hawkeye half-rose, his knife ready, while Strongarm, his loyalty to his young chief overcoming his anger, fired arrow after arrow at the bear. After a mighty struggle, the grizzly was killed. Then Hawkeye stared at his rebel warrior.

11 — There was a long silence. At last Strongarm raised his hand and placed his closed fist on his chest. It was the silent oath of the Blackfeet brave, meaning — "You are my chief. My heart is yours." "It is well," said Hawkeye quietly. They returned home, where a surprise awaited them. A white man, a trader named Cameron, had come in a borrowed canoe to claim his horse and goods. A rope had slipped while he ferried the horse across the river.

12 — Cameron was so pleased to get his horse back that he made the tribe a present of all the toys. But this time Hawkeye made sure it was the little ones who played with them! Strongarm was allowed to keep his "Paleface goddess", but as she had stopped an arrow during the fight with the bear, he was doubtful about her value. Watching the children having fun, Hawkeye said to Cameron — "Paleface toys are good for Indian children — but not for Indian warriors!"

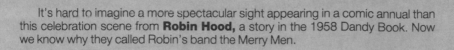
It's hard to imagine a more spectacular sight appearing in a comic annual than this celebration scene from **Robin Hood,** a story in the 1958 Dandy Book. Now we know why they called Robin's band the Merry Men.

SHORT STORIES . . . LONG LAU

THE MAGIC LOLLIPOPS from Beano

KEYHOLE KATE from Dandy

BARNEY BOKO from Dandy

Here's a second helping of strips from the comics' early years. When DANDY and BEANO served up a feast of fun, these were the snack-sized laughs.

MEDDLESOME MATTY from Dandy

GOOD KING COKE from Beano

SEEING DOUBLE?

No! You're seeing doubles — lookalikes of the comic superstars.

To celebrate DANDY'S 50th birthday, B.B.C. TV's "Daytime Live" staged a Comic Lookalike Competition with the winners making a guest appearance in one of their lookalike's comic stories.

In the pages of DANDY, Pete O'Donoghue came chin to chin with **Desperate Dan** and there aren't many hombres tough enough to do that. The historic confrontation took place on 4th June, 1988.

FROM THE FRONT COVER—

THAT'S THE MASKS DESTROYED! NOW IT'S TIME FOR A SHAVE!

SHUCKS! I REALLY DO NEED A SHAVE!

THIS IS THE WINDOW, DAN, AND I'M PETE O'DONOGHUE, YOUR LOOKALIKE!

PLEASED TO MEET YA, PETE, BUT THIS TOWN IS ONLY BIG ENOUGH FOR ONE DESPERATE DAN!

I GET THE MESSAGE! I'LL HEAD BACK TO ST. AUSTELL!

I'M HOLDING THE BUS FOR YOU, PETE!

And that same issue featured **Korky's** feline lookalike Tom Woods. Readers reckoned that **Korky** and Tom made a purrfect pair.

GO DELIVER MEWHERE ELSE.

THIS PARCEL JUST ARRIVED FROM THE DANDY OFFICE, UNCLE KORKY.

IT'S A PICTURE OF TOM WOODS FROM TINGLEY WHO WON DAYTIME LIVE'S KORKY LOOKALIKE CONTEST.

HO-HO! THAT EXPLAINS EVERYTHING.

OPEN IT UP!

Dennis double Jamie Norman came face to face with his hero in the 14th May, 1988, number of BEANO. Jamie was seen on TV next to a **Dennis** cut-out, but menacing is one thing Jamie has no plans to cut out.

HELLO! I'M JAMIE NORMAN FROM HAILSHAM, EAST SUSSEX. I WON THE 'DENNIS LOOK-ALIKE' COMPETITION. I WONDER HOW MUCH I DO LOOK LIKE MY HERO!

WOW! I'M THE SPITTING IMAGE OF HIM!

MIRROR

HAR! HAR! IT IS ME—NOT A REAL MIRROR!

GASP!

MIRROR

SHAKE

NOW, ALL YOU MENACES TURN TO THE BACK PAGE.

And as if appearing in Britain's top comics wasn't reward enough for the lucky winners, TV superstar Leslie Crowther came on down to congratulate them personally.

HYSTERICAL HISTORY

WHAT'S WRONG WITH THIS PICTURE?

OUR ARTIST'S IMPRESSION OF THE BATTLE OF HASTINGS, IN THE YEAR 1066, CONTAINS DOZENS OF DELIBERATE MISTAKES. YOU'LL HAVE A LOT OF FUN TRYING TO SPOT THEM!

If history teachers could make their lessons as much fun as the crazy scene below, they could put their feet up and relax while their pupils laughed their way to the top of the class.
This bizarre battle appeared in the 1961 BEANO Book.

But even these lessons are tame compared with the football game that took place on 10th February, 1962. The CRUNCH match appears overleaf.

HOOTS MON, IT'S DESPERATE MacDAN!

The Texas tough guy took himself all the way to Bonnie Scotland to make an exhibition of himself, and he wasn't alone! The other DANDY and BEANO superstars appeared alongside **Dan** in an exhibition of artists' original drawings from the two comics.

Back in **Dan's** home town of Cactusville a stick-up means trouble, but the tall Texan wore a smile as wide as the Grand Canyon the first time he was stuck-up in Scotland . . . on an art gallery wall.

Thousands of lucky townsfolk saw the exhibition in Dundee, Aberdeen, Stranraer and during a tour of The Highlands. Meanwhile, down south, the DANDY/BEANO Roadshow visited lots of friendly places, telling the two comics' story on a set of colourful panels.

DESPERATE DAN HERE, FOLKS! A'HM SURE LOOKIN' FORWARD TO MEETIN' Y'ALL AT THE STIRLING FESTIVAL!

Dan invited folk to mosey along to the Stirling Festival while standing beside the town's famous Wallace Monument.

Front page appearances by Dan included "What's On In Dundee" and "Gallery" the Aberdeen arts guide.

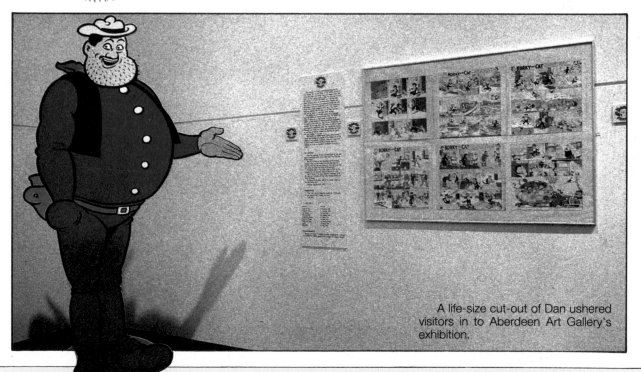

A life-size cut-out of Dan ushered visitors in to Aberdeen Art Gallery's exhibition.

DANDY AND BEANO'S GRAND TOUR

DECEMBER, 1987-JANUARY, 1988
Dundee, Central Library, Wellgate.
Aberdeen Art Gallery.

APRIL, 1988
Stockport Art Gallery.

MAY, 1988
Stranraer Library
Manchester, Arndale Shopping Centre.

JUNE, 1988
Scarborough Arts Extravaganza.
Norwich Tourist Information Centre.
Dundee, Menzieshill Book Fair.
Southampton Central Library.

JULY, 1988
Glasgow, Mitchell Library.
Newcastle Central Library.
Liverpool, Merseyside Festival of Comedy.
Gateshead Metrocentre.
Dundee, The Frigate Unicorn.

AUGUST, 1988
Stirling Festival.
Wick, St Fergus Gallery.
Stockton-On-Tees, Castle Centre.

SEPTEMBER, 1988
Thurso, Swanson Gallery.

OCTOBER, 1988
Kingussie, Iona Gallery.

NOVEMBER, 1988
Paisley Book Fair.

DANDY and BEANO may be great British traditions, more than fifty years old, but they like to keep up to date — their young readers wouldn't have it any other way. In fact, there have been occasions over the years when the two comics were . . .

... AHEAD OF THEIR TIME!

TUNNEL VISION

The Channel Tunnel linking Britain with France won't be completed until well into the 1990s, but way back on 1st November, 1941, **Desperate Dan** was already tunnelling under the sea bed. Of course, the English Channel was too puny for Dan. The DANDY'S mighty man burrowed his way under The Atlantic!

Compare this diagram of The Channel Tunnel with Dan's earlier effort on the right.

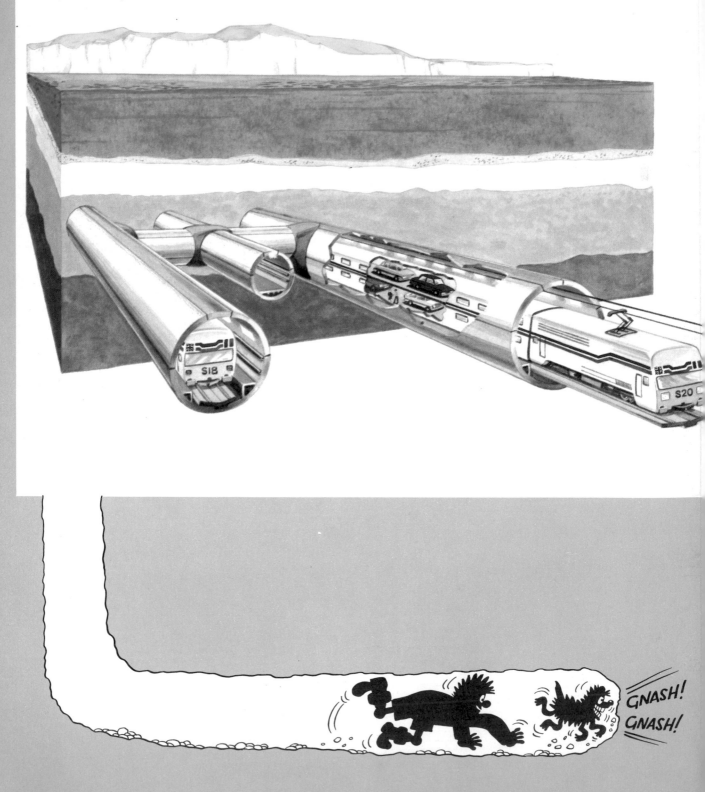

UP UP AND AWAY

Richard Branson soared into the record books, and possibly the history books, with his famous transatlantic hot-air balloon flight in July, 1987. But what inspired this daring scheme?

Was young Richard a fan of **Bandy's Dandy Flying Squad,** and their crazy ballooning exploits, in the 1960 DANDY Annual?

Take a look for yourself and see if Bandy and his pals' flight would encourage you to take off into the wide blue yonder.

THE GREAT FLOOD OF LONDON

London's landmarks were awash in BEANO'S 1960 story, **The Great Flood Of London** and this wasn't pure fiction. The capital city was genuinely vulnerable to flooding and it was only on the completion of the massive Thames Flood Barrier at Woolwich in 1984 that London was made safe from this danger.

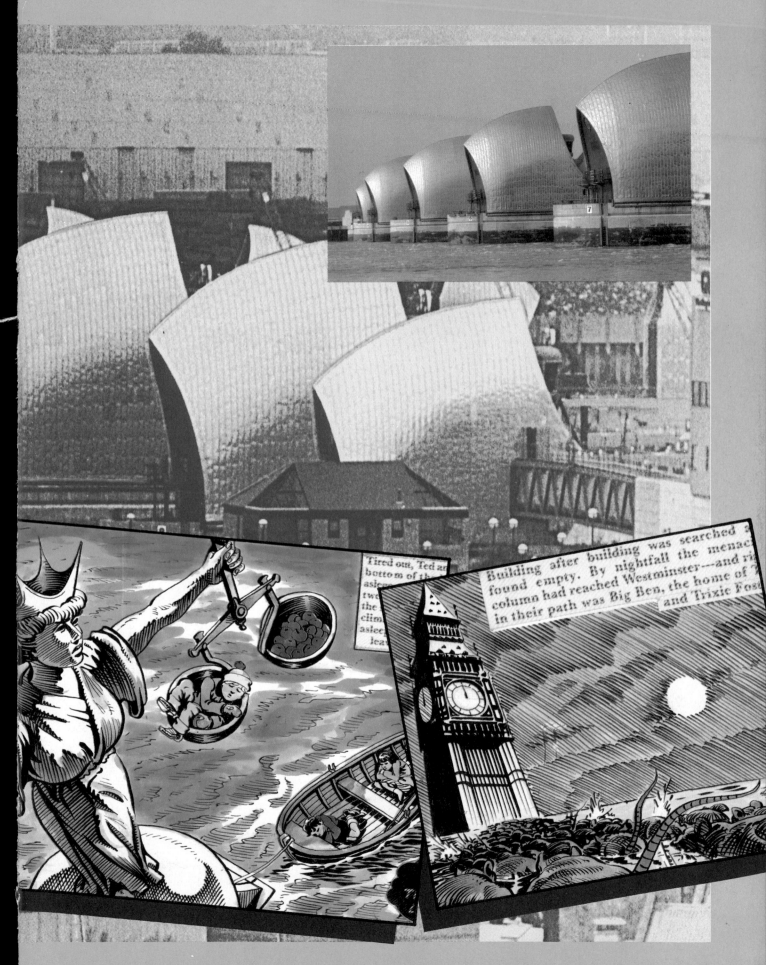

BLACK BOB

TO THE RESCUE!

Time and again, the famous collie from the Scottish Borders made heroic rescues showing no concern for his own safety!

People and animals alike had cause to be grateful to Bob, and agree wholeheartedly that he deserved his title . . . **THE DANDY WONDER DOG!**

GREAT MOMENTS IN HISTORY

4th December, 1987, the day DANDY became fifty years young. And what better way to celebrate than with a giant birthday party in the comic's centre pages.

No party would be complete without guests, and several stars from other comics dropped in to say **"Many happy returns, Dandy!"**

LAUGHING ALL OVER THE WORLD

Wherever you live, in Britain or abroad, you can have DANDY and BEANO delivered to your door every week. Just contact our Subscribers' Department and ask for details:— **Subscribers' Department, D.C. Thomson & Co. Ltd., Bank Street, Dundee, Scotland, DD1 9HU.**